ON
A PIECE OF CHALK
BY THOMAS HENRY HUXLEY

Globigerina bulloides.
One of the present-day
chalk-forming organisms.

ON
A PIECE OF CHALK

by

THOMAS HENRY HUXLEY

Edited & with an Introduction & Notes by

LOREN EISELEY

Drawings by RUDOLF FREUND

CHARLES SCRIBNER'S SONS

New York

CONTENTS

INTRODUCTION
BY LOREN EISELEY

Thomas Henry Huxley. Oil study by Alphonse Legros, 1879.
COURTESY OF THE ROYAL SOCIETY.

Introduction

THERE are really two faces that comprise the face of Thomas Henry Huxley. The one in youth—sensitive, mobile, somewhat sad—is that of a poet. The other in age is less appealing. It could be the face of a great barrister rather than a biologist. The eyes under heavy brows have turned challenging, formidable. They are the eyes of a statesman, a contender for power over the minds of men; the sweet, mobile mouth of youth has become set in grim lines. The whole stance of the body is leonine; the face has evolved into that of a fighter who expects no mercy and gives none. Strength radiates from it, but something has vanished, something that shines wistfully out of the earlier picture—a certain gentleness that must have made the handsome youth strongly attractive to women.

Portraits sometimes make strange alterations in faces, but one is led to think that these pictures do not lie. Instead, the camera has caught a moment of truth. Indeed, in like manner the painter has recorded the transformation of his later features. The portrait painted in age is that of a man capable of devastating criticism, fanatic devotion to work, superb oratorical brilliance. Across his life has fallen tragedy; his only comfort has been exhausting labor performed into the small hours of the night. He has turned upon the dreams and hopes of man the power of a mocking and most penetrating intellect. He embodies man unbeaten, but rendered intellectually impotent before space, time, and the unknowable. He has suffered, indeed he symbolizes, the full religious disillusionment of the later Victorian era. He is of the generation that Charles Darwin both enlightened and spiritually destroyed.

Where others, even Darwin, paused before public opinion, Huxley's utter honesty admitted of no compromise with what he regarded as the truth. Huxley worked for science tirelessly and yet, in the process, the objective student of biography must admit that he became a driven man, capable of honest but merciless ferocity. I have said that Thomas Huxley had two faces. Similarly, he once remarked that literature and science were not two separate things but rather the two sides of a single coin. There remained, therefore, throughout his life a lingering poetic eloquence, a fondness for the literary essay turned to scientific purposes. His work can be matched in his time only by the writings of a naturalist of vastly different temperament and viewpoint, Louis Agassiz, a lingering voice from the pre-Darwinian period, but famous as the primary expositor, though not the only anticipator, of the Ice Age.

In almost everything that mattered these two men were antagonists. It was only as teachers and advocates of the necessity of writing lucidly upon scientific subjects for the layman that they shared a common tradition—a tradition unhappily well-nigh lost or suspect among many scientists today. Yet it was Agassiz and Huxley who, more than any other biologists of the nineteenth century, opened the doorways of thought and bade the common working man to enter and partake unhesitatingly of the delights and responsibilities of learning.

Huxley, born in England in 1825, Agassiz the eloquent Swiss emigrant to America, though diverse in temperament and philosophy, were at one in their enthusiasm for the new education in science and

Thomas Henry Huxley. Photograph by Maull and Polybank, 1857.
COURTESY OF THE BETTMANN ARCHIVE.

in their demand for clarity of expression. In their day science, if it was to receive public acceptance and support, could not afford the luxury of the cloister or the aloof arrogance of an institutionalized bureaucracy. Men had to speak to men. And this is what that notable essay *On a Piece of Chalk*, which is reprinted here, proceeds to do. Before examining its intent, however, it will be well to consider just how Thomas Huxley came by these remarkable gifts of expression and what it was that turned him toward science.

He had, like Darwin, participated as a naturalist and in addition as a medical officer on one of the notable scientific voyages of the century —that of the H.M.S. "Rattlesnake." In Australia, while on that voyage, he met and fell in love with Miss Henrietta Heathorn. The lovers were to be separated by many thousand miles and some years before they were reunited. Huxley's poverty was dire. In a dark hour in 1853 he wrote to his sister Lizzie: "I can get honor in Science, but it doesn't pay. . . . In truth I am often very weary. I begin to doubt whether I have done wisely in giving vent to the cherished tendency toward science which has haunted me ever since my childhood. I may give up the farce altogether—burn my books . . . and take to practice in Australia." Thus wrote the man who was to be one of the leading scientists of the century.

Fortunately, in the following year he received an appointment as lecturer on natural history in the Royal School of Mines in London and was able to eke out his salary with other lectureships. In 1855 he married the girl who had almost precipitated the crisis revealed in his despairing letter to his sister. The publication of *The Origin of Species* was just four years away. Huxley's eloquent defense of Darwin and the rise of the new biology would lend wings to his fame. Though four huge volumes of scientific papers stand to his credit he became known even more widely as an expositor of science to the general public and the most dangerous antagonist a man could face upon the debating platform.

There is no doubt that his ability to sway the minds of men could have been extended to politics if he had been so inclined. A kind of professional duelist's fury drove him incessantly before audiences that the more timid and retiring Darwin could not face. It was by the eloquence of tongue and pen that Thomas Huxley sold Darwin to the general public. In addition, like Agassiz in America, he had a profound influence upon education in general.

On a Piece of Chalk was first delivered in 1868 as a lecture to the working men of Norwich during the meeting of the British Association for the Advancement of Science. It reveals Huxley's natural gift of clear exposition linked with profundity of thought. In his talks to working men he understood instinctively how to take simple things—in this case a well in the earth or a piece of chalk in a carpenter's pocket—and to proceed from the known, by some magical doorway of his own devising, back into the mist of long-vanished geological eras. Lands rise and fall, whole faunas come and go, while the layers of the chalk are built from the efforts of infinitesimal creatures working in almost limitless time. The organisms of the chalk link one fauna to another. Huxley is engaged in subtly demonstrating to his audience, many of whom still believe that giant catastrophes intervened between one epoch and another, that the story of the chalk reveals the genuine continuity of the stream of life—something that is now taken for granted.

We forget that we have in our textbooks the benefit of over 200 years of geological investigation; we forget that it is only recently, through the efforts of such men as Darwin and Huxley and their forerunners, the Englishman Sir Charles Lyell and the Scot James Hutton, that the estimated age of the earth has been enormously extended. Through that well-nigh infinite expanse of time drift the shifting ghostly bodies of creatures no longer living, including ancestral man.

It is not alone "the long snowfall," as Rachel Carson has called it,

in the depths of the sea that swathes and hides the past, however. A few months ago I happened to return to an apartment that had been closed for a year. No maid had dusted, no living person had entered the abandoned rooms. When I prepared to eat a hasty dinner on the white enameled table in the kitchen, I made an interesting discovery. My hands were blackened with dust, though the table to my near-sighted gaze seemed white.

Upon the table, the floor, my books, my desk, had descended a year's rain of invisible motes that human activity normally keeps suspended in the air. I brought a magnifying glass to the table and the dust, as dust will, resolved itself into all manner of tiny organic and inorganic particles. It was the dust that, as surely as the *Globigerine* ooze, would eventually bury man as deeply as the giant lizards of the Cretaceous seas. Dust was black upon my thumb. As an archaeologist I knew its weight when multiplied by centuries. With something of Huxley's weariness I lit a lamp against the fast falling night.

In the year 1801 Samuel Taylor Coleridge created a powerful symbol for all those who recognize the animation of life, but feel at the same time its transience and question its immortality. "I seem," the poet said in a letter to the English chemist Sir Humphry Davy, "to sink in upon myself in a ruin, like a Column of Sand, informed and animated only by a Whirl-Blast of the Desart."

This figure, that is, of form being maintained, while the sundry particles that compose it are being constantly ingested and expelled, was later seized upon by Huxley as analogous to the individual shapes of life itself. Huxley, however, turned to the whirlpool of the river. "Living bodies," he said in 1884, "are just such whirlpools. Matter sets into them in the shape of food, sets out of them in the shape of waste products. Their individuality lies in the constant maintenance of a characteristic form, not in the preservation of material identity. If you dam the stream . . . the whirlpool dies."

In a similar way, in the twentieth century Sir Arthur Keith, the great anatomist, dismissed life as essentially a burning match flame also ingesting and consuming particles through oxidation. When the flame was pinched out, its shape, its reality, vanished. So with the cyclone in the desert, so with the whirlpool in the stream, so also with the flame of life. All three symbols make an admittedly powerful impression upon the imagination. There is, however, one thing warily ignored by the materialist in these three intriguing comparisons. The dust devil has form but no memory, the whirlpool spins without consciousness, that flame that symbolizes the oxidation going on in our bodies is forever without knowledge of itself. By contrast life is not only a vastly more intricate array of organs, but it learns, it can fix its attention or hold amidst all this flux of ingoing and outgoing

particles the fragile pictures of a lifetime. Long-term memory, as one student of time, G. J. Whitrow, the English mathematician, has contended in *The Natural Philosophy of Time*, cannot, in all its aspects, be satisfactorily explained in purely chemical terms.

The nineteenth-century biologists who tried to simplify the creation of life, and who unconsciously sought to combat religious superstition by reducing life's enormous mysteries to the gurgle of bath water running out of a tub, paid an unnecessarily high price for their knowledge of time and organic change. The somber smoke and fog of the industrial age had descended upon them. It haunted Huxley, driven by his own compulsive demon, into overwork. There are passages in his essays that erupt as belligerently as the murky fires of the first blast furnaces. Tension grows among the novelists. Violence and struggle, even prior to the full impact of Darwin, stalk the pages of Emily Brontë's *Wuthering Heights*.

Something had happened to the peaceful life of eighteenth-century rural England. Gilbert White's century of turtles in the garden and owls in the church tower described in the curate-naturalist's writings was passing away and nothing had as yet replaced it. Ahead in the looming future towered fire and rapine in proportions man's darkest past could not emulate. Perhaps in the end the febrile restlessness of Huxley's great creative endeavors can be said to stand as a symbol only reaching its full fruition in the educational and technological achievements of our time. Happiness escaped Huxley as it is escaping our age of power.

In concern about his friend, Darwin once wrote to the botanist Sir Joseph Dalton Hooker: "I fear for Huxley . . . . What I most dislike is this unsettlement for any future scientific or sustaining work: his love of exercising his marvellous intellectual power over men is leading him on and on and on—God knows to where—here he is now at Owens College, Manchester, on Friday, and lecturing to working men at Liverpool yesterday, and to be back in London tonight." In these observant remarks Darwin had touched not alone on the single weakness of a great and essentially good man; he had unconsciously discerned, as had Hooker, the increasing *hubris*, the consuming pride that was to multiply in the lightning-filled laboratories and cyclotrons of the Age of Overkill.

Perhaps the great appeal to the reader of *On a Piece of Chalk* lies in the fact that, as Huxley says, a tiny fossil organism has been made luminous by thought so that it throws light deep into the unknown past. As we have seen, however, there is a daily invisible rain of dust falling with an equal intensity to that of the chalk organisms upon the body of the land. The same geological time of which Huxley speaks, the same shifts of sea level, will bury deep both present cities and our own fragmented bones.

One can only hope that such fossils, like those which fascinated Huxley, will provide illumination to future intelligent beings and justify more than Huxley was able to justify, his belief that "a small beginning has led to a great ending." The ending is not yet, and the dust still falls as it fell so silently for a single year upon my table top. The sample was too small to illuminate the fate of man, but a shadow from the light behind me grew gigantic as I leaned over the table. It may have presaged an omen. Certainly I found my shadow opaque to the clear rays Huxley had cast with such alert penetration into the evolutionary depths of the past. The human shadow remained a shape of darkness no matter how I turned.

Perhaps it was this secret knowledge that haunted in the end that indomitable brain. *"In ultimate analysis everything is incomprehensible,"* he wrote, *"and the whole object of science is simply to reduce the fundamental incomprehensibilities to the smallest possible number."* Under that aegis he labored. Its scars are written upon his face. Thomas Huxley, the educator, perfectly embodied the full light and growing darkness of the scientific age. It is for this reason that there is, to the discerning eye, a kind of illumination emanating from his features as surely as from the buried fossils of the chalk itself. The ravaged prophetic visage of his later years is magnified increasingly across the face of civilization in our time.

On a Piece of Chalk presents an object that in Huxley's own words can be made to shine like the sun and to penetrate by its rays the "abyss of the remote past." If I have spoken of his face as ravaged it is because it is a face of absolute confrontations. It is the duelist's face. There is the final encounter with light and the same equally uncompromising stare before the powers of the night.

There was not time in his life for vacillation. His is a type of face that has tended to vanish into the anonymous grayness and expediency of institutionalized science. Thomas Huxley spoke as a man, not as a team, not as a committee. He used words to reveal and enlighten, not for the devious purposes of obscurity. It is for this reason that he still possesses, long after his death in 1895, and in an age of much more

Thomas Henry Huxley. Photograph by Ernest Edwards from Portraits of Men of Eminence, *Vol. I, London, 1863.* COURTESY OF NEW YORK PUBLIC LIBRARY.

factual knowledge, so powerful a hold over the minds of men. To read him is to hear the voice of an heroic age in science, shaped to a degree and molded by his own endeavor. For good or ill we will not see that age again. Huxley's day and time have gone down into the still-forming chalk as surely as the pterodactyl and the flint ax of our remote precursors. But it is written, as he knew, that we ourselves and all that we possess will follow him. The dust of an eroding planet and the tiny animalcules of the chalk are destined soon or late to entomb us all.

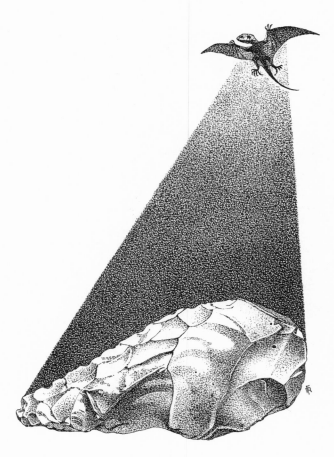

20 *THOMAS HENRY HUXLEY*

ON
A PIECE OF CHALK

On a Piece of Chalk

IF a well were sunk at our feet in the midst of the city of Norwich, the diggers would very soon find themselves at work in that white substance almost too soft to be called rock, with which we are all familiar as *chalk*.

Not only here, but over the whole county of Norfolk, the well sinker might carry his shaft down many hundred feet without coming to the end of the chalk, and on the seacoast, where the waves have pared away the face of the land which breasts them, the scarped faces of the high cliffs are often wholly formed of the same material. Northward, the chalk may be followed as far as Yorkshire; on the south coast it appears abruptly in the picturesque western bays of Dorset and breaks into the Needles of the Isle of Wight; while on the shores of Kent it supplies that long line of white cliffs to which England owes her name of Albion.

Were the thin soil which covers it all washed away, a curved band of white chalk, here broader, and there narrower, might be followed diagonally across England from Lulworth in Dorset to Flamborough Head in Yorkshire—a distance of over 280 miles as the crow flies. From this band to the North Sea, on the east, and the Channel, on the south, the chalk is largely hidden by other deposits, but, except in the Weald of Kent and Sussex,[1] it enters into the very foundation of all the southeastern counties.

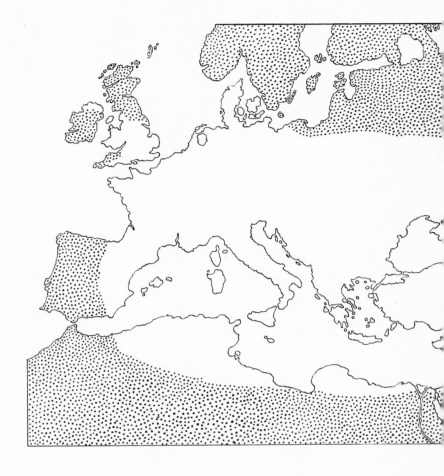

*The region indicated
in white suggests
in rough outline
the extent
of the chalk beds
as known to Huxley.*

Attaining, as it does in some places, a thickness of more than a thousand feet, the English chalk must be admitted to be a mass of considerable magnitude. Nevertheless, it covers but an insignificant portion of the whole area occupied by the chalk formation of the globe, much of which has the same general characters as ours and is found in detached patches, some less, and others more extensive than the English. Chalk occurs in northwest Ireland; it stretches over a large part of France—the chalk which underlies Paris being, in fact, a

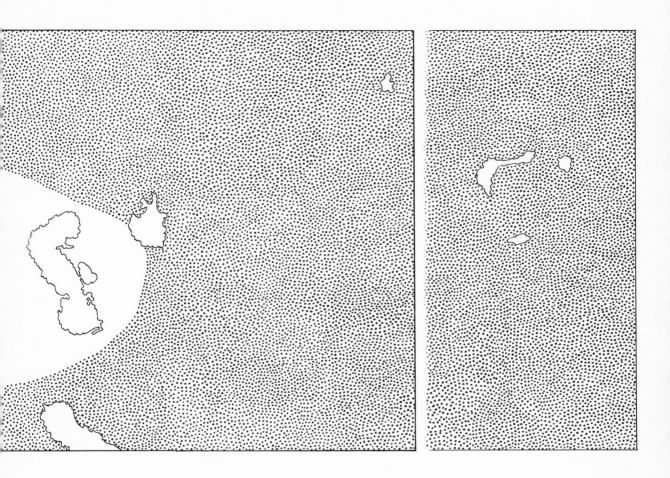

continuation of that of the London basin; it runs through Denmark and Central Europe and extends southward to North Africa, while eastward it appears in the Crimea and in Syria and may be traced as far as the shores of the Sea of Aral, in Central Asia. If all the points at which true chalk occurs were circumscribed, they would lie within an irregular oval about 3,000 miles in long diameter—the area of which would be as great as that of Europe and would many times exceed that of the largest existing inland sea, the Mediterranean.

Thus the chalk is no unimportant element in the masonry of the earth's crust, and it impresses a peculiar stamp, varying with the conditions to which it is exposed, on the scenery of the districts in which it occurs. The undulating downs and rounded coombs,[2] covered with sweet-grassed turf, of our inland chalk country have a peacefully domestic and mutton-suggesting prettiness but can hardly be called grand or beautiful. But on our southern coasts, the wall-sided cliffs, many hundred feet high, with vast needles and pinnacles standing out in the sea, sharp and solitary enough to serve as perches for the wary cormorant, confer a wonderful beauty and grandeur upon the chalk headlands. And, in the East, chalk has its share in the formation of some of the most venerable of mountain ranges, such as the Lebanon.

What is this widespread component of the surface of the earth, and whence did it come?

You may think this no very hopeful inquiry. You may not unnaturally suppose that the attempt to solve such problems as these can lead to no result save that of entangling the inquirer in vague speculations incapable of refutation and of verification. If such were really the case, I should have selected some other subject than a "piece of chalk" for my discourse. But, in truth, after much deliberation I have been unable to think of any topic which would so well enable me to lead you to see how solid is the foundation upon which some of the most startling conclusions of physical science rest.

A great chapter of the history of the world is written in the chalk. Few passages in the history of man can be supported by such an overwhelming mass of direct and indirect evidence as that which testifies to the truth of the fragment of the history of the globe which I hope to enable you to read with your own eyes tonight. Let me add that few chapters of human history have a more profound significance for ourselves. I weigh my words well when I assert that the man who should know the true history of the bit of chalk which every carpenter carries about in his breeches pocket, though ignorant of all other history, is likely, if he will think his knowledge out to its ultimate results, to have a truer, and therefore a better conception of this wonderful universe and of man's relation to it than the most learned student who is deep-read in the records of humanity and ignorant of those of nature.

The language of the chalk is not hard to learn, not nearly so hard as Latin, if you only want to get at the broad features of the story it has to tell, and I propose that we now set to work to spell that story out together.

We all know that if we "burn" chalk the result is quicklime. Chalk, in fact, is a compound of carbonic-acid gas and lime, and when you make it very hot the carbonic acid flies away and the lime is left.

By this method of procedure we see the lime, but we do not see the carbonic acid. If, on the other hand, you were to powder a little chalk and drop it into a good deal of strong vinegar, there would be a great bubbling and fizzing and, finally, a clear liquid, in which no sign of chalk would appear. Here you see the carbonic acid in the bubbles; the lime, dissolved in the vinegar, vanishes from sight. There are a great many other ways of showing that chalk is essentially nothing but carbonic acid and quicklime. Chemists enunciate the result of all the experiments which prove this by stating that chalk is almost wholly composed of carbonate of lime.

28 *THOMAS HENRY HUXLEY*

It is desirable for us to start from the knowledge of this fact, though it may not seem to help us very far toward what we seek. For carbonate of lime is a widely spread substance and is met with under very various conditions. All sorts of limestones are composed of more or less pure carbonate of lime. The crust which is often deposited by waters which have drained through limestone rocks in the form of what are called stalagmites and stalactites is carbonate of lime. Or, to take a more familiar example, the fur on the inside of a tea kettle is carbonate of lime [3]; and, for anything chemistry tells us to the contrary, the chalk might be a kind of gigantic fur upon the bottom of the earth kettle, which is kept pretty hot below.

Let us try another method of making the chalk tell us its own history. To the unassisted eye chalk looks simply like a very loose and open kind of stone. But it is possible to grind a slice of chalk down so thin that you can see through it—until it is thin enough, in fact, to be examined with any magnifying power that may be thought desirable. A thin slice of the fur of a kettle might be made in the same way. If it were examined microscopically, it would show itself to be a more or less distinctly laminated mineral substance and nothing more.

But the slice of chalk presents a totally different appearance when placed under the microscope. The general mass of it is made up of very minute granules, but embedded in this matrix are innumerable bodies, some smaller and some larger, but, on a rough average, not more than a hundredth of an inch in diameter, having a well-defined shape and structure. A cubic inch of some specimens of chalk may contain hundreds of thousands of these bodies compacted together with incalculable millions of the granules.

The examination of a transparent slice gives a good notion of the manner in which the components of the chalk are arranged and of their relative proportions. But, by rubbing up some chalk with a brush in water and then pouring off the milky fluid so as to obtain sediments of different degrees of fineness, the granules and the minute rounded

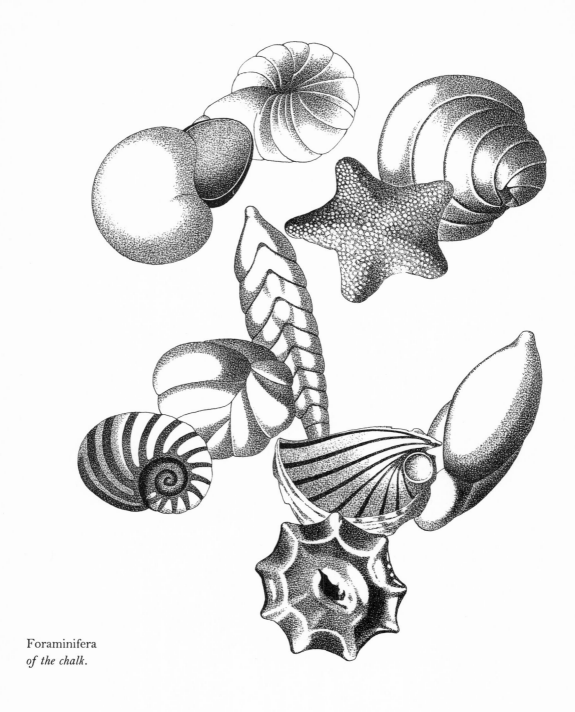

Foraminifera
of the chalk.

bodies may be pretty well separated from one another and submitted to microscopic examination, either as opaque or as transparent objects. By combining the views obtained in these various methods, each of the rounded bodies may be proved to be a beautifully constructed calcareous fabric, made up of a number of chambers communicating freely with one another. The chambered bodies are of various forms. One of the commonest is something like a badly grown raspberry, being formed of a number of nearly globular chambers of different sizes congregated together. It is called *Globigerina*, and some specimens of chalk consist of little else than *Globigerinæ* and granules. Let us fix our attention upon the *Globigerina*. It is the spoor of the game we are tracking. If we can learn what it is and what are the conditions of its existence, we shall see our way to the origin and past history of the chalk.

A suggestion which may naturally enough present itself is that these curious bodies are the result of some process of aggregation which has taken place in the carbonate of lime; that, just as in winter the rime on our windows simulates the most delicate and elegantly arborescent foliage—proving that the mere mineral water may, under certain conditions, assume the outward form of organic bodies, so this mineral substance, carbonate of lime, hidden away in the bowels of the earth, has taken the shape of these chambered bodies. I am not raising a merely fanciful and unreal objection. Very learned men in former days have even entertained the notion that all the formed things found in rocks are of this nature, and if no such conception is at present held to be admissible, it is because long and varied experience has now shown that mineral matter never does assume the form and structure we find in fossils. If anyone were to try to persuade you that an oyster shell (which is also chiefly composed of carbonate of lime) had crystallized out of sea water, I suppose you would laugh at the absurdity. Your laughter would be justified by the fact that all experience tends to show that oyster shells are formed by the agency of oysters and in no other way. And if there were no better reasons, we should be justi-

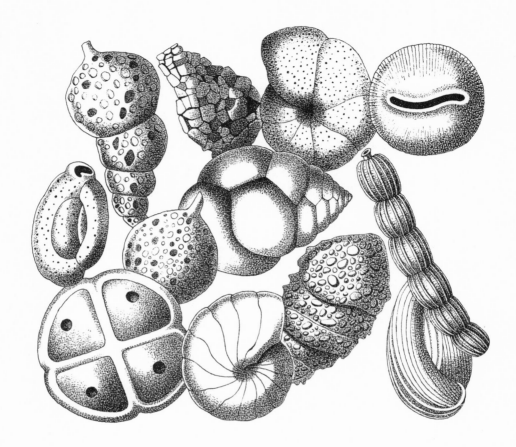

fied, on like grounds, in believing that *Globigerina* is not the product of anything but vital activity.

Happily, however, better evidence in proof of the organic nature of the *Globigerinæ* than that of analogy is forthcoming. It so happens that calcareous skeletons, exactly similar to the *Globigerinæ* of the chalk, are being formed at the present moment by minute living creatures which flourish in multitudes, literally more numerous than the sands of the seashore, over a large extent of that part of the earth's surface which is covered by the ocean.

The history of the discovery of these living *Globigerinæ* and of the part which they play in rock building is singular enough. It is a discovery which, like others of no less scientific importance, has arisen, incidentally, out of work devoted to very different and exceedingly practical interests. When men first took to the sea, they speedily learned to look out for shoals and rocks, and the more the burden of their ships increased, the more imperatively necessary it became for sailors to ascertain with precision the depth of the waters they traversed. Out of this necessity grew the use of the lead and sounding line and, ultimately, marine surveying, which is the recording of the form of coasts and of the depth of the sea, as ascertained by the sounding lead upon charts.

At the same time, it became desirable to ascertain and to indicate the nature of the sea bottom, since this circumstance greatly affects its goodness as holding ground for anchors. Some ingenious tar, whose name deserves a better fate than the oblivion into which it has fallen, attained this object by "arming" the bottom of the lead with a lump of grease, to which more or less of the sand or mud, or broken shells, as the case might be, adhered and was brought to the surface. But, however well adapted such an apparatus might be for rough nautical purposes, scientific accuracy could not be expected from the armed lead, and to remedy its defects (especially when applied to sounding in great depths) Lieutenant Brooke of the American Navy some years

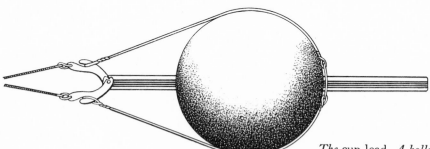

The cup lead. *A hollow ball operated by a mechanism which enabled a bottom sample of the oceanic ooze to be collected.*

ago invented a most ingenious machine by which a considerable portion of the superficial layer of the sea bottom can be scooped out and brought up from any depth to which the lead descends. In 1853, Lieutenant Brooke obtained mud from the bottom of the North Atlantic between Newfoundland and the Azores at a depth of more than 10,000 feet, or two miles, by the help of this sounding apparatus. The specimens were sent for examination to Ehrenberg of Berlin and to Bailey of West Point,[4] and those able microscopists found that this deep-sea mud was almost entirely composed of the skeletons of living organisms—the greater proportion of these being just like the *Globigerinæ* already known to occur in the chalk.

Thus far, the work had been carried on simply in the interests of science, but Lieutenant Brooke's method of sounding acquired a high commercial value when the enterprise of laying down the telegraph cable between this country and the United States was undertaken. For it became a matter of immense importance to know not only the depth of the sea over the whole line along which the cable was to be laid, but the exact nature of the bottom, so as to guard against chances of cutting or fraying the strands of that costly rope. The Admiralty consequently ordered Captain Dayman, an old friend and shipmate of mine, to ascertain the depth over the whole line of the cable and to bring back specimens of the bottom. In former days, such a command as this might have sounded very much like one of the impossible things which the young prince in the fairy tales is ordered to do before he can obtain the hand of the princess. However, in the months of June and July, 1857, my friend performed the task assigned to him with great expedition and precision, without, so far as I know, having met with any reward of that kind. The specimens of Atlantic mud which he procured, were sent to me to be examined and reported upon.*

* See Appendix to Captain Dayman's *Deep-sea Soundings in the North Atlantic Ocean between Ireland and Newfoundland, made in H.M.S. "Cyclops."* Published by order of the Lords Commissioners of the Admiralty, 1858. They have since formed the subject of an elaborate Memoir by Messrs. Parker and Jones, published in the *Philosophical Transactions* for 1865.

The "Great Eastern" engaged in laying the first Atlantic cable. A sperm whale is represented below.

The result of all these operations is that we know the contours and the nature of the surface soil covered by the North Atlantic for a distance of 1,700 miles from east to west as well as we know that of any part of the dry land. It is a prodigious plain—one of the widest and most even plains in the world. If the sea were drained off, you might drive a wagon all the way from Valentia on the west coast of Ireland to Trinity Bay in Newfoundland. And, except upon one sharp incline about 200 miles from Valentia, I am not quite sure that it would even be necessary to put the skid on, so gentle are the ascents and descents

The known contours of the North Atlantic seabed. The heavy dark line indicates the route of the first North Atlantic cable from Valentia, Ireland, to Trinity Bay in Newfoundland. A mountainous ridge, unmentioned by Huxley, bisects the "prodigious plain."

upon that long route. From Valentia the road would lie downhill for about 200 miles to the point at which the bottom is now covered by 1,700 fathoms of sea water. Then would come the central plain, more than a thousand miles wide, the inequalities of the surface of which would be hardly perceptible, though the depth of water upon it now varies from 10,000 to 15,000 feet, and there are places in which Mont Blanc might be sunk without showing its peak above water. Beyond this the ascent on the American side commences and gradually leads, for about 300 miles, to the Newfoundland shore.

Almost the whole of the bottom of this central plain (which extends for many hundred miles in a north and south direction) is covered by a fine mud, which, when brought to the surface, dries into a greyish white friable substance. You can write with this on a blackboard, if you are so inclined, and to the eye it is quite like very soft, grayish chalk. Examined chemically, it proves to be composed almost wholly of carbonate of lime, and if you make a section of it in the same way as that of the piece of chalk was made and view it with the microscope, it presents innumerable *Globigerinæ* embedded in a granular matrix. Thus this deep-sea mud is substantially chalk. I say substantially because there are a good many minor differences, but as these have no bearing on the question immediately before us—which is the nature of the *Globigerinæ* of the chalk—it is unnecessary to speak of them.

Globigerinæ of every size, from the smallest to the largest, are associated together in the Atlantic mud, and the chambers of many are filled by a soft animal matter. This soft substance is, in fact, the remains of the creature to which the *Globigerina* shell, or rather skeleton, owes its existence—and which is an animal of the simplest imaginable description. It is, in fact, a mere particle of living jelly without defined parts of any kind—without a mouth, nerves, muscles, or distinct organs, and only manifesting its vitality to ordinary observation by thrusting out and retracting from all parts of its surface, long filamentous processes which serve for arms and legs. Yet this amorphous particle, devoid of everything which, in the higher animals, we call organs, is capable of feeding, growing, and multiplying; of separating from the ocean the small proportion of carbonate of lime which is dissolved in sea water; and of building up that substance into a skeleton for itself, according to a pattern which can be imitated by no other known agency.

The notion that animals can live and flourish in the sea at the vast depths from which apparently living *Globigerinæ* have been brought up does not agree very well with our usual conceptions respecting the conditions of animal life, and it is not so absolutely impossible as it might at first sight appear to be that the *Globigerinæ* of the Atlantic sea bottom do not live and die where they are found.

As I have mentioned, the soundings from the great Atlantic plain are almost entirely made up of *Globigerinæ*, with the granules which have been mentioned, and some few other calcareous shells, but a small percentage of the chalky mud—perhaps at most some five per cent of it—is of a different nature and consists of shells and skeletons composed of silex, or pure flint. These silicious bodies belong partly to the lowly vegetable organisms which are called *Diatomaceæ*, and partly to the minute, and extremely simple, animals termed *Radiolaria*. It is quite certain that these creatures do not live at the bottom of the ocean, but at its surface—where they may be obtained in prodigious numbers by the use of a properly constructed net. Hence it follows that

these silicious organisms, though they are not heavier than the lightest dust, must have fallen, in some cases, through 15,000 feet of water before they reached their final resting place on the ocean floor. And considering how large a surface these bodies expose in proportion to their weight, it is probable that they occupy a great length of time in making their burial journey from the surface of the Atlantic to the bottom.

But if the *Radiolaria* and diatoms are thus rained upon the bottom of the sea from the superficial layer of its waters in which they pass their lives, it is obviously possible that the *Globigerinæ* may be similarly derived, and if they were so, it would be much more easy to understand how they obtain their supply of food than it is at present. Nevertheless, the positive and negative evidence all points the other way. The skeletons of the full-grown, deep-sea *Globigerinæ* are so remarkably solid and heavy in proportion to their surface as to seem little fitted for floating, and, as a matter of fact, they are not to be found along with the diatoms and *Radiolaria* in the uppermost stratum of the open ocean. It has been observed, again, that the abundance of *Globigerinæ* in proportion to other organisms of like kind increases with the depth of the sea and that deep-water *Globigerinæ* are larger than those which live in shallower parts of the sea, and such facts negative the supposition that these organisms have been swept by currents from the shallows into the deeps of the Atlantic. It therefore seems to be hardly doubtful that these wonderful creatures live and die at the depths in which they are found.*

* During the cruise of H.M.S. "Bulldog," commanded by Sir Leopold McClintock in 1860, living starfishes were brought up, clinging to the lowest part of the sounding line, from a depth of 1,260 fathoms, midway between Cape Farewell, in Greenland, and the Rockall banks. Dr. Wallich ascertained that the sea bottom at this point consisted of the ordinary *Globigerina* ooze and that the stomachs of the starfishes were full of *Globigerinæ*. This discovery removes all objections to the existence of living *Globigerinæ* at great depths which are based upon the supposed difficulty of maintaining animal life under such conditions, and it throws the burden of proof upon those who object to the supposition that the *Globigerinæ* live and die where they are found.

However, the important points for us are that the living *Globigerinæ* are exclusively marine animals, the skeletons of which abound at the bottom of deep seas, and that there is not a shadow of reason for believing that the habits of the *Globigerinæ* of the chalk differed from those of the existing species. But if this be true, there is no escaping the conclusion that the chalk itself is the dried mud of an ancient deep sea.

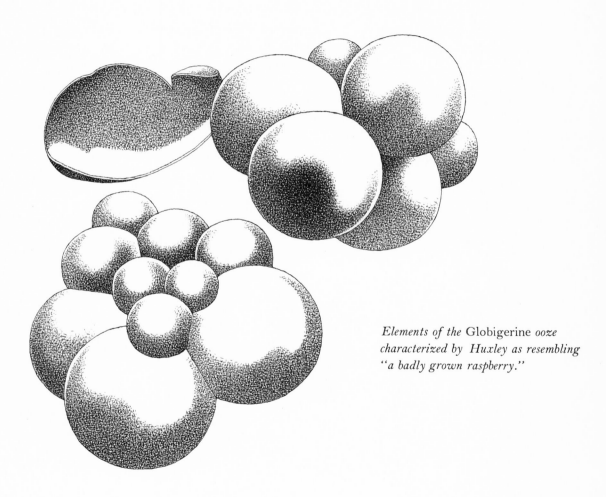

Elements of the Globigerine *ooze characterized by Huxley as resembling "a badly grown raspberry."*

Coccoliths now known to be the remnants of unicellular algae.

In working over the soundings collected by Captain Dayman, I was surprised to find that many of what I have called the "granules" of that mud were not, as one might have been tempted to think at first, the mere powder and waste of *Globigerinæ*, but that they had a definite form and size. I termed these bodies *coccoliths* and doubted their organic nature. Dr. Wallich verified my observation and added the interesting discovery that, not unfrequently, bodies similar to these coccoliths were aggregated together into spheroids which he termed *coccospheres*.[5]

42 *THOMAS HENRY HUXLEY*

So far as we knew, these bodies, the nature of which is extremely puzzling and problematical, were peculiar to the Atlantic soundings. But, a few years ago Mr. Sorby,[6] in making a careful examination of the chalk by means of thin sections and otherwise, observed, as Ehrenberg had done before him, that much of its granular basis possesses a definite form. Comparing these formed particles with those in the Atlantic soundings, he found the two to be identical and thus proved that the chalk, like the surroundings, contains these mysterious coccoliths and coccospheres. Here was a further and most interesting confirmation, from internal evidence, of the essential identity of the chalk with modern deep-sea mud. *Globigerinæ*, coccoliths, and coccospheres are found as the chief constituents of both and testify to the general similarity of the conditions under which both have been formed.*

The evidence furnished by the hewing, facing, and superposition of the stones of the pyramids that these structures were built by men has no greater weight than the evidence that the chalk was built by *Globigerinæ*, and the belief that those ancient pyramid builders were terrestrial and air-breathing creatures like ourselves is not better based than the conviction that the chalk makers lived in the sea. But as our belief in the building of the pyramids by men is not only grounded on the internal evidence afforded by these structures, but gathers strength from multitudinous collateral proofs and is clinched by the total absence of any reason for a contrary belief, so the evidence drawn from the *Globigerinæ* that the chalk is an ancient sea bottom is fortified by innumerable independent lines of evidence; and our belief in the truth of the conclusion to which all positive testimony tends receives the like negative justification from the fact that no other hypothesis has a shadow of foundation.

* I have recently traced out the development of the coccoliths from a diameter of $\frac{1}{7000}$ of an inch up to their largest size (which is about $\frac{1}{1600}$), and no longer doubt that they are produced by independent organisms, which, like the *Globigerinæ*, live and die at the bottom of the sea.

It may be worthwhile briefly to consider a few of these collateral proofs that the chalk was deposited at the bottom of the sea. The great mass of the chalk is composed, as we have seen, of the skeletons of *Globigerinæ* and other simple organisms embedded in granular matter. Here and there, however, this hardened mud of the ancient sea reveals the remains of higher animals which have lived and died and left their hard parts in the mud, just as the oysters die and leave their shells behind them in the mud of the present seas.

There are, at the present day, certain groups of animals which are never found in fresh waters, being unable to live anywhere but in the sea. Such are the corals, those corallines which are called *Polyzoa*, those creatures which fabricate the lamp shells, and are called *Brachiopoda*, the pearly nautilus, and all animals allied to it, and all the forms of sea urchins and starfishes. Not only are all these creatures confined to salt water at the present day, but, so far as our records of the past go, the conditions of their existence have been the same; hence, their occurrence in any deposit is as strong evidence as can be obtained that that deposit was formed in the sea. Now the remains of animals of all the kinds which have been enumerated occur in the chalk, in greater or less abundance, while not one of those forms of shellfish which are characteristic of fresh water has yet been observed in it.

When we consider that the remains of more than 3,000 distinct species of aquatic animals have been discovered among the fossils of the chalk, that the great majority of them are of such forms as are now met with only in the sea, and that there is no reason to believe that any one of them inhabited fresh water—the collateral evidence that the chalk represents an ancient sea bottom acquires as great force as the proof derived from the nature of the chalk itself. I think you will now allow that I did not overstate my case when I asserted that we have as strong grounds for believing that all the vast area of dry land at present occupied by the chalk was once at the bottom of the sea as we have for any matter of history whatever, while there is no justification for any other belief.

No less certain it is that the time during which the countries we now call southeast England, France, Germany, Poland, Russia, Egypt, Arabia, Syria were more or less completely covered by a deep sea was of considerable duration. We have already seen that the chalk is, in places, more than a thousand feet thick. I think you will agree with me that it must have taken some time for the skeletons of animalcules of a hundredth of an inch in diameter to heap up such a mass as that.

I have said that throughout the thickness of the chalk the remains of other animals are scattered. These remains are often in the most exquisite state of preservation. The valves of the shellfishes are commonly adherent; the long spines of some of the sea urchins, which would be detached by the smallest jar, often remain in their places. In a word, it is certain that these animals have lived and died when the place which they now occupy was the surface of as much of the chalk as had then been deposited and that each has been covered up by the layer of *Globigerina* mud, upon which the creatures embedded a little higher up have, in like manner, lived and died. But some of these remains prove the existence of reptiles of vast size in the chalk sea. These lived their time and had their ancestors and descendants, which assuredly implies time, reptiles being of slow growth.

There is more curious evidence, again, that the process of covering up, or, in other words, the deposit of *Globigerina* skeletons, did not go on very fast. It is demonstrable that an animal of the Cretaceous sea might die, that its skeleton might lie uncovered upon the sea bottom long enough to lose all its outward coverings and appendages by putrefaction, and that, after this had happened, another animal might attach itself to the dead and naked skeleton, might grow to maturity, and might itself die before the calcareous mud had buried the whole.

Cases of this kind are admirably described by Sir Charles Lyell.[7] He speaks of the frequency with which geologists find in the chalk a fossilized sea urchin, to which is attached the lower valve of a *Crania*. This is a kind of shellfish, with a shell composed of two pieces, of which, as in the oyster, one is fixed and the other free.

"The upper valve is almost invariably wanting, though occasionally found in a perfect state of preservation in the white chalk at some distance. In this case, we see clearly that the sea urchin first lived from youth to age, then died and lost its spines, which were carried away. Then the young *Crania* adhered to the bared shell, grew and perished in its turn; after which, the upper valve was separated from the lower, before the Echinus became enveloped in chalky mud."*[8]

A specimen in the Museum of Practical Geology, in London, still further prolongs the period which must have elapsed between the death of the sea urchin and its burial by the *Globigerinæ*. For the outward face of the valve of a *Crania*, which is attached to a sea urchin (*Micraster*), is itself overrun by an encrusting coralline, which spreads thence over more or less of the surface of the sea urchin. It follows that after the upper valve of the *Crania* fell off, the surface of the attached valve must have remained exposed long enough to allow of the growth of the whole coralline, since corallines do not live embedded in mud.

The progress of knowledge may, one day, enable us to deduce from such facts as these the maximum rate at which the chalk can have accumulated and thus to arrive at the minimum duration of the chalk period.[9] Suppose that the valve of the *Crania* upon which a coralline has fixed itself in the way just described is so attached to the sea urchin that no part of it is more than an inch above the face upon which the sea urchin rests. Then, as the coralline could not have fixed itself if the *Crania* had been covered up with chalk mud and could not have lived had itself been so covered, it follows that an inch of chalk mud could not have accumulated within the time between the death and decay of the soft parts of the sea urchin and the growth of the coralline to the full size which it has attained. If the decay of the soft parts of the sea urchin; the attachment, growth to maturity, and decay of the *Crania*; and the subsequent attachment and growth of the coralline, took a year (which is a low estimate enough), the accumulation of the inch

* *Elements of Geology*, by Sir Charles Lyell, Bart. F.R.S., p. 23.

of chalk must have taken more than a year; and the deposit of 1,000 feet of chalk must, consequently, have taken more than 12,000 years.

The foundation of all this calculation is, of course, a knowledge of the length of time the *Crania* and the coralline needed to attain their full size, and, on this head, precise knowledge is at present wanting. But there are circumstances which tend to show that nothing like an inch of chalk has accumulated during the life of a *Crania*, and, on any probable estimate of the length of that life, the chalk period must have had a much longer duration than that thus roughly assigned to it.

Thus, not only is it certain that the chalk is the mud of an ancient sea bottom, but it is no less certain that the chalk sea existed during an extremely long period, though we may not be prepared to give a precise estimate of the length of that period in years. The relative duration is clear, though the absolute duration may not be definable. The attempt to affix any precise date to the period at which the chalk sea began, or ended, its existence is baffled by difficulties of the same kind. But the relative age of the Cretaceous epoch may be determined with as great ease and certainty as the long duration of that epoch.

You will have heard of the interesting discoveries recently made in various parts of western Europe of flint implements obviously worked into shape by human hands under circumstances which show conclusively that man is a very ancient denizen of these regions.[10] It has been proved that the whole populations of Europe, whose existence has been revealed to us in this way, consisted of savages, such as the Esquimos are now, that in the country which is now France, they hunted the reindeer and were familiar with the ways of the mammoth[11] and the bison. The physical geography of France was in those days different from what it is now—the river Somme, for instance, having cut its bed a hundred feet deeper between that time and this, and it is probable that the climate was more like that of Canada or Siberia than that of western Europe.

The existence of these people is forgotten even in the traditions of the oldest historical nations. The name and fame of them had utterly vanished until a few years back, and the amount of physical change which has been effected since their day renders it more than probable that, venerable as are some of the historical nations, the workers of the chipped flints of Hoxne or of Amiens [12] are to them, as they are to us, in point of antiquity. But, if we assign to these hoary relics of long-vanished generations of men the greatest age that can possibly be claimed for them, they are not older than the drift, or boulder clay,

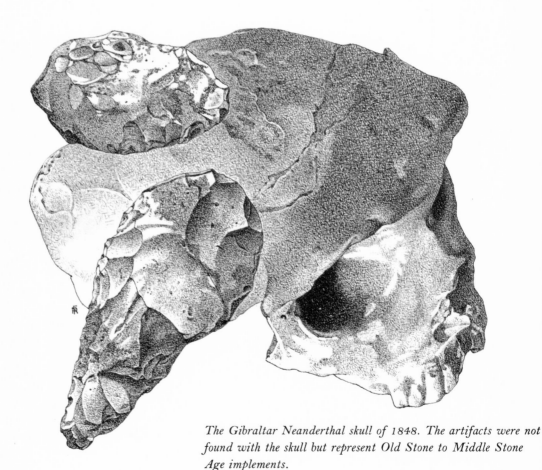

The Gibraltar Neanderthal skull of 1848. The artifacts were not found with the skull but represent Old Stone to Middle Stone Age implements.

which, in comparison with the chalk, is but a very juvenile deposit. You need go no further than your own seaboard for evidence of this fact. At one of the most charming spots on the coast of Norfolk, Cromer, you will see the boulder clay forming a vast mass which lies upon the chalk and must, consequently, have come into existence after it. Huge boulders of chalk are, in fact, included in the clay and have evidently been brought to the position they now occupy by the same agency as that which has planted blocks of syenite [13] from Norway side by side with them.

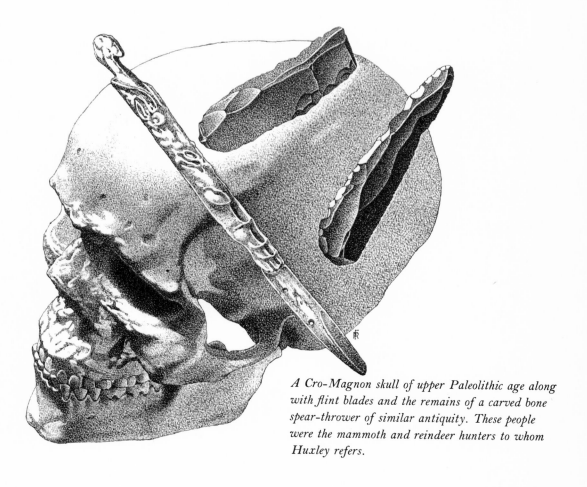

A Cro-Magnon skull of upper Paleolithic age along with flint blades and the remains of a carved bone spear-thrower of similar antiquity. These people were the mammoth and reindeer hunters to whom Huxley refers.

The chalk, then, is certainly older than the boulder clay. If you ask how much, I will again take you no further than the same spot upon your own coasts for evidence. I have spoken of the boulder clay and drift as resting upon the chalk. That is not strictly true. Interposed between the chalk and the drift is a comparatively insignificant layer containing vegetable matter. But that layer tells a wonderful history. It is full of stumps of trees standing as they grew. Fir trees are there with their cones, and hazel bushes with their nuts; there stand the stools of oak and yew trees, beeches and alders. Hence this stratum is appropriately called the "forest bed."

It is obvious that the chalk must have been upheaved and converted into dry land before the timber trees could grow upon it. As the bolls of some of these trees are from two to three feet in diameter, it is no less clear that the dry land thus formed remained in the same condition for long ages. And not only do the remains of stately oaks and well-grown firs testify to the duration of this condition of things, but additional evidence to the same effect is afforded by the abundant remains of elephants, rhinoceroses, hippopotamuses, and other great wild beasts, which it has yielded to the zealous search of such men as the Rev. Mr. Gunn. When you look at such a collection as he has formed, and bethink you that these elephantine bones did veritably carry their owners about, and these great grinders crunch, in the dark woods of which the forest bed is now the only trace, it is impossible not to feel that they are as good evidence of the lapse of time as the annual rings of the tree stumps.

Thus there is a writing upon the wall of cliffs at Cromer, and whoso runs may read it. It tells us, with an authority which cannot be impeached, that the ancient sea bed of the chalk sea was raised up and remained dry land until it was covered with forest, stocked with the great game the spoils of which have rejoiced your geologists. How long it remained in that condition cannot be said, but "the whirligig of time brought its revenges"[14] in those days as in these. That dry

*Examples
of the
primeval
elephants
ranging from
earlier
to
Ice Age forms.*

land, with the bones and teeth of generations of long-lived elephants hidden away among the gnarled roots and dry leaves of its ancient trees, sank gradually to the bottom of the icy sea, which covered it with huge masses of drift and boulder clay. Sea beasts, such as the walrus, now restricted to the extreme north, paddled about where birds had twittered among the topmost twigs of the fir trees. How long this state of things endured we know not, but at length it came to an end. The upheaved glacial mud hardened into the soil of modern Norfolk. Forests grew once more, the wolf and the beaver replaced the reindeer and the elephant, and at length what we call the history of England dawned.

Thus you have, within the limits of your own county, proof that the chalk can justly claim a very much greater antiquity than even the oldest physical traces of mankind. But we may go further and demonstrate, by evidence of the same authority as that which testifies to the existence of the father of men, that the chalk is vastly older than Adam himself. The Book of Genesis informs us that Adam, immediately upon his creation, and before the appearance of Eve, was placed in the Garden of Eden. The problem of the geographical position of Eden has greatly vexed the spirits of the learned in such matters, but there is one point respecting which, so far as I know, no commentator has ever raised a doubt. This is that of the four rivers which are said to run out of it, Euphrates and Hiddekel are identical with the rivers now known by the names of Euphrates and Tigris. But the whole country in which these mighty rivers take their origin and through which they run is composed of rocks which are either of the same age as the chalk or of later date. So that the chalk must not only have been formed, but, after its formation, the time required for the deposit of these later rocks and for their upheaval into dry land must have elapsed before the smallest brook which feeds the swift stream of "the great river, the river of Babylon," began to flow.

Thus, evidence which cannot be rebutted and which need not be strengthened, though if time permitted I might indefinitely increase its quantity, compels you to believe that the earth, from the time of the chalk to the present day, has been the theater of a series of changes as vast in their amount as they were slow in their progress. The area on which we stand has been first sea and then land for at least four alternations and has remained in each of these conditions for a period of great length.

Nor have these wonderful metamorphoses of sea into land and of land into sea been confined to one corner of England. During the chalk period, or Cretaceous epoch, not one of the present great physical features of the globe was in existence. Our great mountain ranges, Pyrenees, Alps, Himalayas, Andes, have all been upheaved since the chalk was deposited and the Cretaceous sea flowed over the sites of Sinai and Ararat. All this is certain because rocks of Cretaceous, or still later, date have shared in the elevatory movements which gave rise to these mountain chains and may be found perched up, in some cases, many thousand feet high upon their flanks. And evidence of equal cogency demonstrates that, though, in Norfolk, the forest bed rests directly upon the chalk, yet it does so not because the period at which

A Cretaceous forest scene.

56

the forest grew immediately followed that at which the chalk was formed, but because an immense lapse of time, represented elsewhere by thousands of feet of rock, is not indicated at Cromer.

I must ask you to believe that there is no less conclusive proof that a still more prolonged succession of similar changes occurred before the chalk was deposited. Nor have we any reason to think that the first term in the series of these changes is known. The oldest sea beds preserved to us are sands, and mud, and pebbles, the wear and tear of rocks which were formed in still older oceans.

*Living animals are
shaded; extinct forms
are represented in outline.*

But, great as is the magnitude of these physical changes of the world, they have been accompanied by a no less striking series of modifications in its living inhabitants. All the great classes of animals, beasts of the field, fowls of the air, creeping things, and things which dwell in the waters, flourished upon the globe long ages before the chalk was deposited. Very few, however, if any, of these ancient forms of animal life were identical with those which now live. Certainly not one of the higher animals was of the same species as any of those now in existence. The beasts of the field, in the days before the chalk, were not our beasts of the field, nor the fowls of the air such as those which the eye of man has seen flying, unless his antiquity dates infinitely further back than we at present surmise. If we could be carried back into those times, we should be as one suddenly set down in Australia before it was colonized. We should see mammals, birds, reptiles, fishes, insects, snails, and the like, clearly recognizable as such, and yet not one of them would be just the same as those with which we are familiar, and many would be extremely different.

A restored
Rhamphorhynchus, *one*
of the pterodactyls.

61

From that time to the present, the population of the world has undergone slow and gradual, but incessant, changes. There has been no grand catastrophe—no destroyer has swept away the forms of life of one period and replaced them by a totally new creation, but one species has vanished and another has taken its place; creatures of one type of structure have diminished, those of another have increased as time has passed on. And thus, while the differences between the living creatures of the time before the chalk and those of the present day appear startling if placed side by side, we are led from one to the other by the most gradual progress if we follow the course of nature through the whole series of those relics of her operations which she has left behind. It is by the population of the chalk sea that the ancient and the modern inhabitants of the world are most completely connected. The groups which are dying out flourish, side by side, with the groups which are now the dominant forms of life. Thus the chalk contains remains of those strange flying and swimming reptiles, the ptero-dactyl, the ichthyosaurus, and the plesiosaurus, which are found in no later deposits but abounded in preceding ages. The chambered shells called ammonites and belemnites,[15] which are so characteristic of the period preceding the Cretaceous, in like manner die with it.

But, among these fading remainders of a previous state of things, are some very modern forms of life, looking like Yankee peddlers among a tribe of Red Indians. Crocodiles of modern type appear; bony fishes, many of them very similar to existing species, almost supplant the forms of fish which predominate in more ancient seas; and many kinds of living shellfish first become known to us in the chalk. The vegetation acquires a modern aspect. A few living animals are not even distinguishable as species from those which existed at that remote epoch.[16] The *Globigerina* of the present day, for example, is not different specifically from that of the chalk, and the same may be said of many other *Foraminifera*. I think it probable that critical and unprejudiced examination will show that more than one species of much higher animals have had a similar longevity, but the only example which I can at present give confidently is the snake's-head lamp shell (*Terebratulina caput serpentis*), which lives in our English seas and abounded (as *Terebratulina striata* of authors) in the chalk.[17]

The longest line of human ancestry must hide its diminished head before the pedigree of this insignificant shellfish. We Englishmen are proud to have an ancestor who was present at the Battle of Hastings. The ancestors of *Terebratulina caput serpentis* may have been present at a battle of *Ichthyosauria*[18] in that part of the sea which, when the chalk was forming, flowed over the site of Hastings. While all around has changed, this *Terebratulina* has peacefully propagated its species from generation to generation, and stands to this day, as a living testimony to the continuity of the present with the past history of the globe.

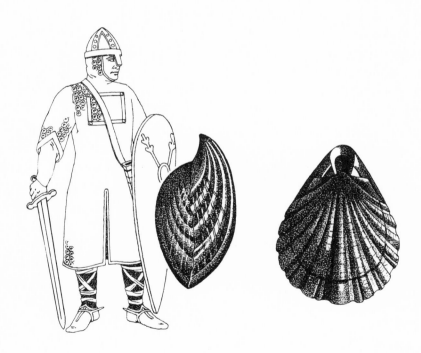

Giant's Causeway, Ireland. A cooled basaltic intrusion of lava from the earth's interior; such volcanic phenomena along with the insensible erosion of millenia play a role in altering the surface and elevation of the land.

Up to this moment I have stated, so far as I know, nothing but well-authenticated facts and the immediate conclusions which they force upon the mind. But the mind is so constituted that it does not willingly rest in facts and immediate causes but seeks always after a knowledge of the remoter links in the chain of causation.

Taking the many changes of any given spot of the earth's surface, from sea to land and from land to sea, as an established fact, we cannot refrain from asking ourselves how these changes have occurred. And when we have explained them—as they must be explained—by the alternate slow movements of elevation and depression which have affected the crust of the earth, we go still further back and ask, Why these movements?

I am not certain that any one can give you a satisfactory answer to that question. Assuredly I cannot. All that can be said, for certain, is, that such movements are part of the ordinary course of nature, inasmuch as they are going on at the present time. Direct proof may

be given that some parts of the land of the northern hemisphere are at this moment insensibly rising and others insensibly sinking, and there is indirect but perfectly satisfactory proof that an enormous area now covered by the Pacific has been deepened thousands of feet since the present inhabitants of that sea came into existence. Thus there is not a shadow of a reason for believing that the physical changes of the globe in past times have been effected by other than natural causes. Is there any more reason for believing that the concomitant modifications in the forms of the living inhabitants of the globe have been brought about in other ways?

Before attempting to answer this question, let us try to form a distinct mental picture of what has happened in some special case. The crocodiles are animals which, as a group, have a very vast antiquity. They abounded ages before the chalk was deposited; they throng the rivers in warm climates at the present day. There is a difference in the form of the joints of the backbone and in some minor particulars between the crocodiles of the present epoch and those which lived before the chalk, but, in the Cretaceous epoch, as I have already mentioned, the crocodiles had assumed the modern type of structure. Notwithstanding this, the crocodiles of the chalk are not identically the same as those which lived in the times called "older Tertiary," which succeeded the Cretaceous epoch; and the crocodiles of the older Tertiaries are not identical with those of the newer Tertiaries, nor are these identical with existing forms.[19] I leave open the question whether particular species may have lived on from epoch to epoch. But each epoch has had its peculiar crocodiles; though all, since the chalk, have belonged to the modern type and differ simply in their proportions and in such structural particulars as are discernible only to trained eyes.

How is the existence of this long succession of different species of crocodiles to be accounted for? Only two suppositions seem to be

66

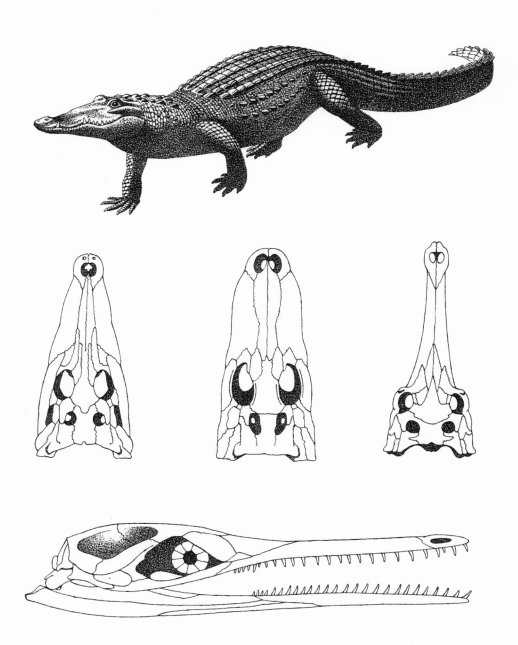

open to us: Either each species of crocodile has been specially created, or it has arisen out of some preexisting form by the operation of natural causes. Choose your hypothesis; I have chosen mine. I can find no warranty for believing in the distinct creation of a score of successive species of crocodiles in the course of countless ages of time. Science gives no countenance to such a wild fancy, nor can even the perverse ingenuity of a commentator pretend to discover this sense in the simple words in which the writer of Genesis records the proceedings of the fifth and sixth days of the Creation.

On the other hand, I see no good reason for doubting the necessary alternative, that all these varied species have been evolved from preexisting crocodilian forms, by the operation of causes as completely a part of the common order of nature as those which have effected the changes of the inorganic world. Few will venture to affirm that the reasoning which applies to crocodiles loses its force among other animals, or among plants. If one series of species has come into existence by the operation of natural causes, it seems folly to deny that all may have arisen in the same way.

A small beginning has led us to a great ending. If I were to put the bit of chalk with which we started into the hot but obscure flame of burning hydrogen, it would presently shine like the sun. It seems to me that this physical metamorphosis is no false image of what has been the result of our subjecting it to a jet of fervent, though nowise brilliant, thought tonight. It has become luminous, and its clear rays, penetrating the abyss of the remote past, have brought within our ken some stages of the evolution of the earth. And in the shifting "without haste, but without rest" [20] of the land and sea, as in the endless variation of the forms assumed by living beings, we have observed nothing but the natural product of the forces originally possessed by the substance of the universe.

NOTES BY LOREN EISELEY

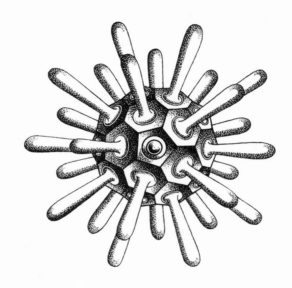

A rhabdolith. *Another microorganism from the surface water whose skeletons form part of "the long snowfall" into the abyssal depths of the sea.*

Notes by Loren Eiseley

1 The Weald of Kent, Surrey, and Sussex Counties is a large, wooded area, formerly heavily forested.

2 In England, "downs" are hilly, uncultivated pasture land. A "coomb" is a hollow or valley among hills.

3 The "fur," as Huxley indicated, is carbonate of lime, which is precipitated over the course of time on the interior surface of a much-used tea kettle. The amount of encrustation may vary from locality to locality, depending upon the amount of lime in the water.

4 Christian Gottfried Ehrenberg (1795–1875) was a German naturalist known especially for his studies of infusoria, that is, microscopic organisms. Jacob Whitman Bailey (1811–1857), a teacher of chemistry, mineralogy, and geology at West Point, was a pioneer of American science. He was especially noted for his microscopical studies.

5 Huxley termed the disklike organic remains found in deep-sea dredging coccoliths. They are now regarded as the calcareous remains of certain types of oceanic plankton. Today, these tiny skeletons are generally re-

ferred to by geologists as *tests*. Coccospheres were simply spheroidal aggregations of coccoliths. Actually, the creatures lived in the upper waters of the sea. Only the intricate shells or tests fell in a long, unending rain into the deep abyss. This, however, was not fully understood in Huxley's time. Most of the Cretaceous chalk is composed of an extinct genus known as *Gümbelina*. See note 6.

6 Henry Clifton Sorby (1826–1908), the English geologist, invented a method of making thin rock slices for microscopic investigation. He was noted for his work in microscopic petrology. In 1861 he concluded that the coccoliths of the English chalk were part of the external skeletons of living organisms instead of inorganic "crystalloids." The living coccospheres are now known to be unicellular algae belonging to the genus *Chyrsophyceæ*. They are primitive relatives of the seaweeds and swim freely near the surface of the sea. Most of the Cretaceous chalk forms have perished, but one has persisted to the present day. A number of new species emerged in post-Cretaceous times.

7 Sir Charles Lyell (1797–1875) was one of the most outstanding British geologists of the nineteenth century. His *Principles of Geology* (1830–33)

Sir Charles Lyell.

72

exercised a profound influence upon the thinking of Charles Darwin. The two men became fast friends, and there is no doubt that Lyell's advice and counsel were highly esteemed by the younger man. Lyell played a major role in convincing the public of the enormous range of geological time. Without this extension of time, Darwin's theory of organic change by the natural selection of fortuitous variations would not have proved acceptable to science.

8 Echinus is simply a synonym for the sea urchin. It is a spined, marine animal that often lives between the area of high and low tides. In various forms it extends far into the fossil past.

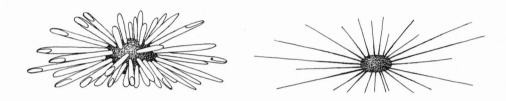

9 The duration of the Cretaceous period is generally estimated today at about 60 million years. It was the period that marked the end of the Age of Reptiles. Shortly after its close the mammals began to increase in size and radiate into the environments from which the dinosaurs had vanished. The late Cretaceous is also noted as a time of vast intrusion of shallow seas upon the continents.

10 Man is now known to have been a toolmaker for well over a million years; that is, for more than the entire duration of Ice Age time. The oldest and crudest finds to date have turned up in South and East Africa. Less is known of man in Europe before the Second Interglacial, one of the periods occurring between glacial advances. It must be kept in mind that Europe is only a minor peninsular protrusion from the Asiatic land mass. Thus

though crude tools and implements reveal man's early presence here, it is most unlikely that man's more remote history can be deciphered from so small an area.

11 Mammoths are extinct members of the elephant family, that is, temperate- and arctic-zone elephants. They were also present in great numbers in North America and were hunted here by the first human intruders. The hairy mammoth is represented in European cave paintings and formed part of the food supply of Ice Age man. In both America and the Old World they seem to have disappeared at the close of the Pleistocene period, which saw the rise of man. Doubtless man played a part in their disappearance, but it may well be that the increasing warmth and other environmental changes in the areas the mammoths frequented contributed to their final extinction. The term *mammoth* must not be misconstrued. Some were larger of tusk and body than the living elephant, but the lay public has frequently exaggerated their actual size. Today's elephants, however, represent only a fading remnant of a once widely dispersed and highly successful form of life that arose in Africa, spread widely across Europe and Asia, and at some point in the geological past successfully crossed the then existing land bridge into the New World.

12 In a commercial clay pit at Hoxne in Suffolk, England, the archaeologist John Frere (1740–1807), one of the earliest students of prehistory, unearthed in 1797 a flint implement in association with the remains of extinct animals. Frere ascribed his find to "a very remote period," but he was in advance of his time, and his discovery was ignored. The site is certainly lower Paleolithic. Similarly, at Amiens in France, hand axes of lower Paleolithic age had been uncovered. In Huxley's time the full succession of ice advances and retreats along with their corresponding index fossils and artifacts had not been established. Indeed, archaeologists are still laboring at this task today. We can only say that the men of Amiens and Hoxne lived at a time when England was still part of the continent of Europe—a time hundreds of thousands of years removed from us. Of this, both the implements and the associated deposits inform us.

13 Syenite is a crystalline rock allied to granite in structure. Today, we know that the great ice sheets transported rocks and boulders for hundreds of miles.

14 "And thus the whirligig of time brings in his revenges." William Shakespeare, *Twelfth Night*, Act V, Scene i.

15 Ammonites are shelled cephalopods related to the modern octopus and squid. The coiled shells of ammonites were once thought by the unlettered to be coiled, petrified snakes. Belemnites are straight, smooth cylinders a few inches long, representing a part of the internal structure of a Mesozoic cuttlefish. Like ancient human hand axes they have been referred to as "thunderbolts" or "thunderstones" by those ignorant of their real origin.

16 Huxley is here simply referring to what today we would speak of as "living fossils," that is, creatures who, with little or no modification, have lived through long geological periods in which other forms of life have either become extinct or greatly modified.

17 The information upon *Terebratulina caput serpentis* as discussed by Huxley seems to have been drawn from an early (1851–1855) work by Thomas Davidson. Today this term is applied to a different coiled mollusc.

18 *Ichthyosaurs* were marine reptiles of fishlike form and about the size of modern porpoises. Like modern whales they were air breathers, and, like the whales, they were one-time land vertebrates that had returned to the sea.

19 The older Tertiary today would include the Paleocene, Eocene, and possibly Oligocene epochs. The newer Tertiary would most certainly include the Miocene and Pliocene.

20 "Without haste! without rest!" Johann Wolfgang von Goethe, "Haste Not, Rest Not," Stanza 1.

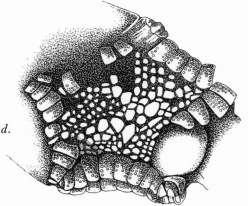

*A fossil starfish
from the white chalk of England.*

APPENDIX

Time Scale	ERAS	Duration of periods		PERIODS
				Recent
0 10 20 30 40 50 60	CENOZOIC 60 to 80 million years duration	60		Pleistocene Oligocene Pliocene Eocene Miocene Paleocene
70 80 90 100	MESOZOIC 140 million years duration	60		Cretaceous
150		35		Jurassic
		45		Triassic
200	PALEOZOIC 350 million years duration	25		Permian
250		20		Pennsylvanian
		30		Mississippian
300		65		Devonian
350		35		Silurian
400		75		Ordovician
450 500		90		Cambrian
	PROTEROZOIC ARCHAEOZOIC			Approximately 3 billion years duration

After Colbert

DOMINANT ANIMAL LIFE

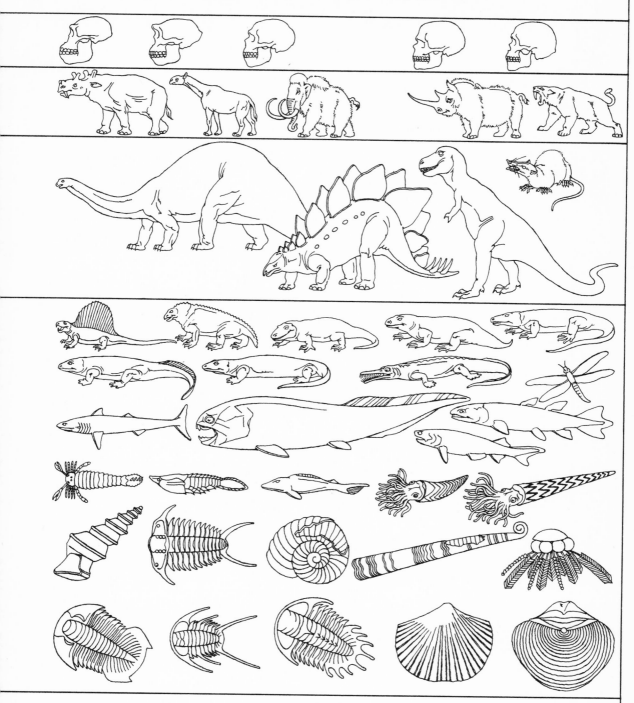

BEGINNINGS OF LIFE

SELECTED BIBLIOGRAPHY

Selected Bibliography

BOOKS BY THOMAS HENRY HUXLEY

Collected Essays. London: Macmillan & Co.

Volume I. *Method and Results* (1893)

II. *Darwiniana* (1893)

III. *Science and Education* (1893)

IV. *Science and the Hebrew Tradition* (1893)

V. *Science and the Christian Tradition* (1894)

VI. *Hume, with Helps to the Study of Berkeley* (1894)

VII. *Man's Place in Nature* (1894)

VIII. *Discourses, Biological and Geological* (1894)

IX. *Evolution and Ethics and Other Essays* (1894)

The Scientific Memoirs of Thomas Henry Huxley. Edited by Michael Foster and Edwin Ray Lankester. 4 vols. London: Macmillan & Co. 1898–1902. Supplementary vol. 1903.

BOOKS ABOUT THOMAS HENRY HUXLEY

Ainsworth-Davies, James Richard: *Thomas H. Huxley.* London: J. M. Dent & Co., 1907.

Ayres, Clarence Edwin: *Huxley*. New York: W. W. Norton & Co., Inc., 1932.

Bibby, Cyril: *T. H. Huxley: Scientist, Humanist, and Educator*. New York: Horizon Press, 1960.

Clodd, Edward: *Thomas Henry Huxley*. New York: Dodd, Mead, & Co., 1902.

Foster, Sir Michael: *Royal Society Obituary Notice of T. H. Huxley*. ("Obituary Notices of the Royal Society," Vol. LIX.) London, n.d.

Huxley, Aldous Leonard: *T. H. Huxley as a Man of Letters*. London: Macmillan & Co., 1932.

Huxley, Leonard: *Life and Letters of Thomas Henry Huxley*. London: Macmillan & Co., 1900.

Mitchell, Sir Peter Chalmers: *Thomas Huxley; a Sketch of His Life and Work*. New York, London: G. P. Putnam's Sons, 1900.

Osborn, Henry Fairfield: *Huxley and Education*. New York: Charles Scribners Sons, 1910.

Peterson, Houston: *Huxley, Prophet of Science*. London, New York: Longmans Green and Co., 1932.

BOOKS BY THOMAS HENRY HUXLEY IN PRINT

Man's Place in Nature. Ann Arbor, Mich.: University of Michigan Press, 1959.

Selections from the Essays of T. H. Huxley. Edited by Alburey Castell. New York: Appleton-Century-Crofts, 1948.

INDEX

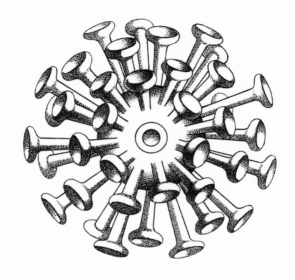

A curious microscopic plant
form that differs from the rhabdolith
on page 70.

Index

ABOUT THE EDITOR

LOREN EISELEY, University Professor of Anthropology and the History of Science at the University of Pennsylvania, is, like Thomas Huxley, known as a literary naturalist. His books on natural science include *The Immense Journey, Darwin's Century,* and *The Firmament of Time.* He is also the author of a number of scientific and literary articles, many of which have been reprinted in anthologies.

During his youth in Nebraska he spent many hours in the local museum studying the bones of mammoths, and his interest in evolution, which parallels Huxley's, stems from this time.

Professor Eiseley has been the recipient of fellowships, honorary degrees, and awards and prizes for his published work. Among the latter are the Phi Beta Kappa Science Prize, the Athenaeum Society of Philadelphia Award, the John Burroughs Medal, the du Nouy Foundation Award, and the Philadelphia Arts Festival Award for Literature. For his distinguished teaching and administrative career he received a Special Citation presented by the Department of Public Instruction, Commonwealth of Pennsylvania, in 1962.

ABOUT THE ILLUSTRATOR

RUDOLF FREUND, who died in 1969, was well known as a science illustrator; his major interest was natural history. He illustrated numerous articles in such national magazines as *Scientific American* and *Life.* He also contributed drawings to books by Joseph Wood Krutch, Donald Culross Peattie, and other distinguished naturalists.

His illustrations, exemplary for their accuracy of detail as well as their aesthetic appeal, won many awards, including the Gold Medal of the 16th International Congress of Zoology and the Certificate of Merit of the 37th Annual National Exhibition of Advertising and Editorial Art and Design.